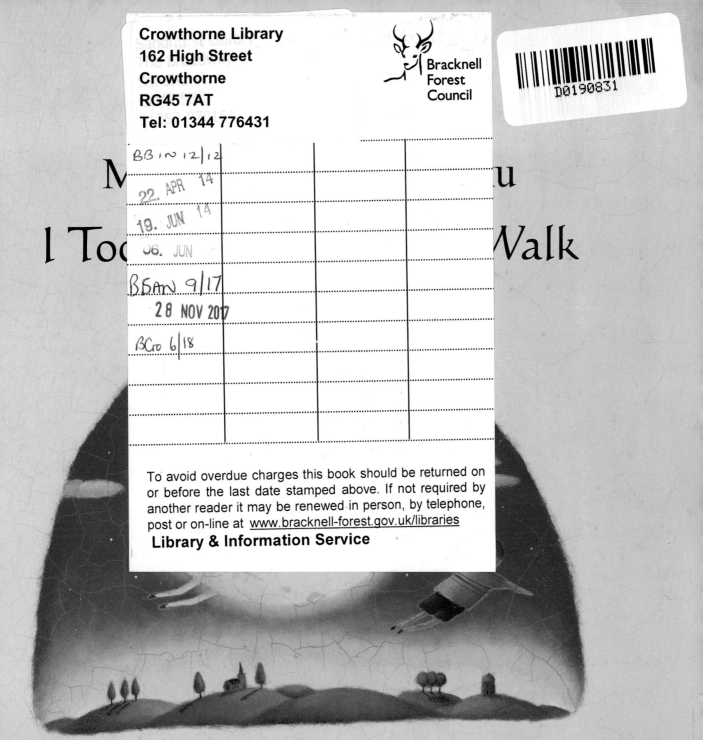

M... u
l Too... Walk

Written by Carolyn Curtis
Illustrated by Alison Jay

Slovakian translation by Eva Tomova

I took the Moon for a walk last night.
It followed behind like a still summer kite,

Zobral som Mesiačik na prechádzku minulú noc.
Nasledoval ma stále ako šarkan,

Though there wasn't a string or a tail in sight
when I took the Moon for a walk.

Hociako nebolo tam ani živej duše
Keď som zobral Mesiačik na prechádzku.

I carried my blue torch just in case
the Moon got scared and hid its face.

Niesol som moju modru lampičku len v prípade
Mesiačik sa zľakol a skryl svoju tvár.

Ale vyliezol spoza mrakov, ktoré
boli jemné ako čipka keď som
zobral Mesiačik na prechádzku.

But it peeked through clouds
that were fragile as lace
When I took the Moon for a walk.

I warned the Moon to rise a bit higher
so it wouldn't get hooked on a church's tall spire,

Upozornil som Mesiačik výjsť trošku vyššie
tak, že sa nechytí na špicatej veži,

While the neighbourhood dogs made a train-whistle choir
when I took the Moon for a walk.

Kým susedové psy brechali ako rútiaci sa vlak
keď som zobral Mesiačik na prechádzku.

We tiptoed through grass where the night crawlers creep
when the rust-bellied robins have all gone to sleep,

My sme išli po špičkách cez trávu, kde sa plýžia nočné chrobáky
kde vtáčiky s hrdzavou hruďou idú spinkať,

A Mesiačik vyvolal rosu, tak trávu vyzerala ako uplakaná
Keď som zobral Mesiačik na prechádzku.

And the Moon called the dew so the grass seemed to weep
When I took the Moon for a walk.

Jazdili sme ako na hojdalke, keď
som vykopol svoje nohy vysoko
A Mesiačik sa ma opýtal lietať,

We raced for the swings,
where I kicked my feet high
And imagined the Moon had
just asked me to fly,

Hand holding hand through the starry night sky when I took the Moon for a walk.

Ruka v ruke cez hviezdnatú oblohu
keď som zobral Mesiačik na prechádzku.

We danced 'cross the bridge where the smooth waters flow.
The Moon was above and the Moon was below,

Sme tancovali cez most, kde voda tečie.
Mesiačik bol nadomnou, Mesiačik bol podomnou,

Jasnosť medzi nimi odrážala žiaru
Keď som zobral Mesiačik na
prechádzku.

And bright in between them
I echoed in their glow
When I took the Moon for a walk.

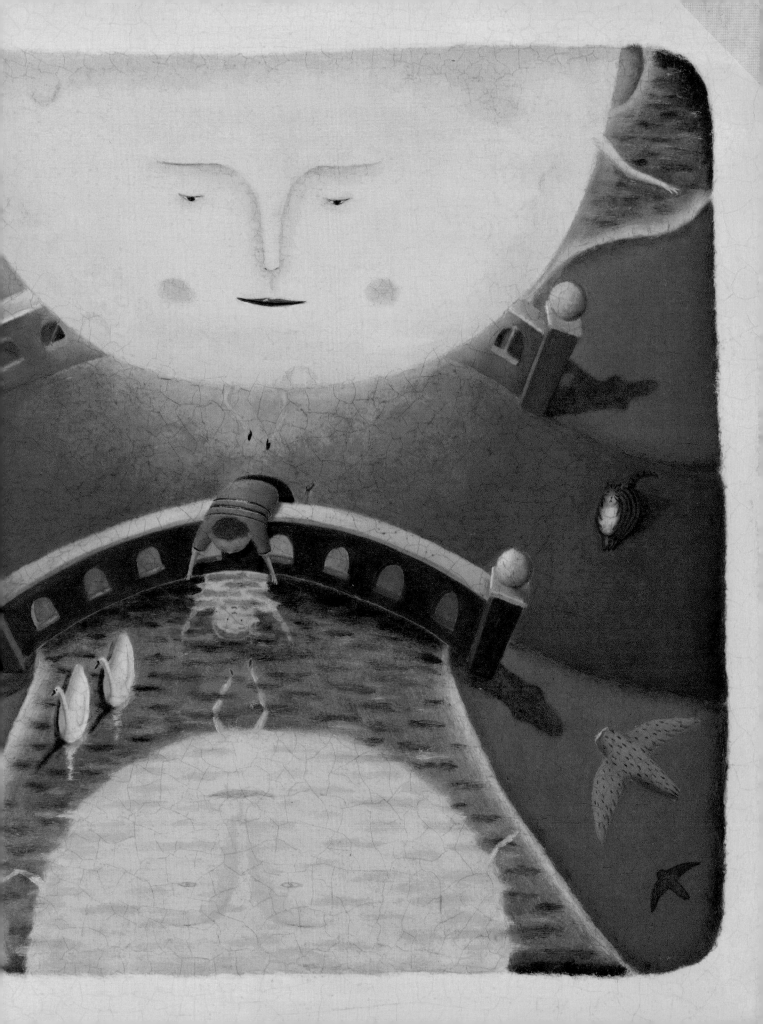

Then as we turned back, the Moon kept me in sight.
It followed me home and stayed there all night,

Potom ako sme sa otočili späť, udržiaval nadomnou svoj zrak.
Nasledoval ma až domov a zostal tam celú noc,

And thanked me by sharing its sweet sleepy light
when I took the Moon for a walk.

A ďakoval mi za delenie sladkého uspávajúceho svetla
keď som zobral Mesiačik na prechádzku.

The Mysterious Moon

What do you see when you look at the moon? Children who live in Europe and the United States imagine that they see a man when they look at the moon. Children in Japan and India see a rabbit, and children in Australia see a kitten. But all children, no matter where they live, look up in wonder at the same moon.

The moon is primarily made of rock with a small iron core. It creates no light of its own, but reflects sunlight.

The shape of the moon seems to change during the month because the sunlight strikes the moon at different angles as it travels through space. These shapes are called 'phases'. Here are some of the phases of the moon:

New Moon   Crescent Moon   Half Moon   Gibbous Moon   Full Moon

When the moon is growing larger in the sky, we say that it is 'waxing'. When it is growing smaller, we say that it is 'waning'.

For people all over the world, the moon has always been an important way to measure time. Although the solar calendar has become the standard international way of doing this, many people still use lunar, or moon, calendars.

The moon can be a friend to farmers and gardeners - those who follow tradition know that the best time to sow seeds and transplant young shoots is when the moon is waxing.

Moon festivals are celebrated in many societies. The Chinese Moon Festival is held during the Harvest Moon - the full moon that rises in mid-autumn.

Many Celtic and Native American festivals are also held at the time of the Harvest Moon, when the people give thanks for the harvest and for all living things on earth.

The World at Night

If you took the moon for a walk through your neighbourhood, what would you show it? What would you hear, and what would you see?

Wherever you are, you would probably see some nocturnal creatures - mammals, birds and insects that usually sleep during the day and come out at night. They are especially adapted to life under the moon and stars:

Cats have eyes that see very well in the dark.

Rabbits have large ears that capture sound across long distances.

Bats use sounds and echoes to help them fly safely and find food.

Fireflies light up at night so that they can find each other.

Owls have necks that can turn right around and huge, flat eyes that enable them to see other creatures that are far away.

Some flowers are nocturnal too. They bloom and release their fragrance after dark.

And although you are asleep during the night, your mind is not! During the day, your waking, or conscious, mind is active, but when you sleep, your dreaming, or unconscious, mind is busy. So, the world at night is not so quiet as it seems!

For my nephew Christopher, *who first walked with the moon*
and my mother Estella, *who held his hand*
For my father Harold, *the star we steer by*
and Lucan, *my sun*
and, of course, for Emilie, *for Everything* - C.C.

The author extends heartfelt thanks to the society of Children's Book Writers and Illustrators for generous support in the form of
a Barbara Karlin Grant, WarmLines Parent Resources, Jane Yolen, the Jeff Kelly and Newton Library Critique Groups, and Alison Keehn.

For Mark, happy moon walking, love from Alison.

Mantra Lingua TalkingPEN
Global House
303 Ballards Lane
London N12 8NP
www.mantralingua.com
www.talkingpen.co.uk